Ann Bu

CANYON COUNTRY

Contents

Cover painting: *The Grand Canyon of Yellowstone* (1893) by Thomas Moran (1837-1926).

ISBN 0-8497-9712-8

WP579

Ann Buys is an independent studio teacher currently teaching in St. George, Utah. Her active professional career includes performing for her church as organist, serving as a choral director, and writing and arranging church music.

Ann is a Nationally Certified Teacher of Music and is an active member of the Utah Music Teachers Association and the Music Teachers National Association. After conducting a workshop at the 1990 Utah Music Teachers Association Convention and the 1991 Music Teachers Convention on "Working Toward Certification", Ann became active in expanding the Utah Music Teachers Association student testing program.

In addition to her teaching and professional career, Ann's musical influence has touched her family. Five of her children are pianists and one is a vocalist. Other Ann Buys collections published by the Neil A. Kjos Music Company include *Gaelic Cellebration, A Joyful Christmas,* and *Moods for Christmas.*

ANASAZI*

Ann Buys

*Anasazi is Navajo for "ancient ones." Ancestors of Pueblo Indians, the Anasazi lived in the desert canyon areas of what are now Arizona, New Mexico, Colorado, Utah, and northern Mexico.

24
cresc.
28
f
mf
32
36
mp
f
40

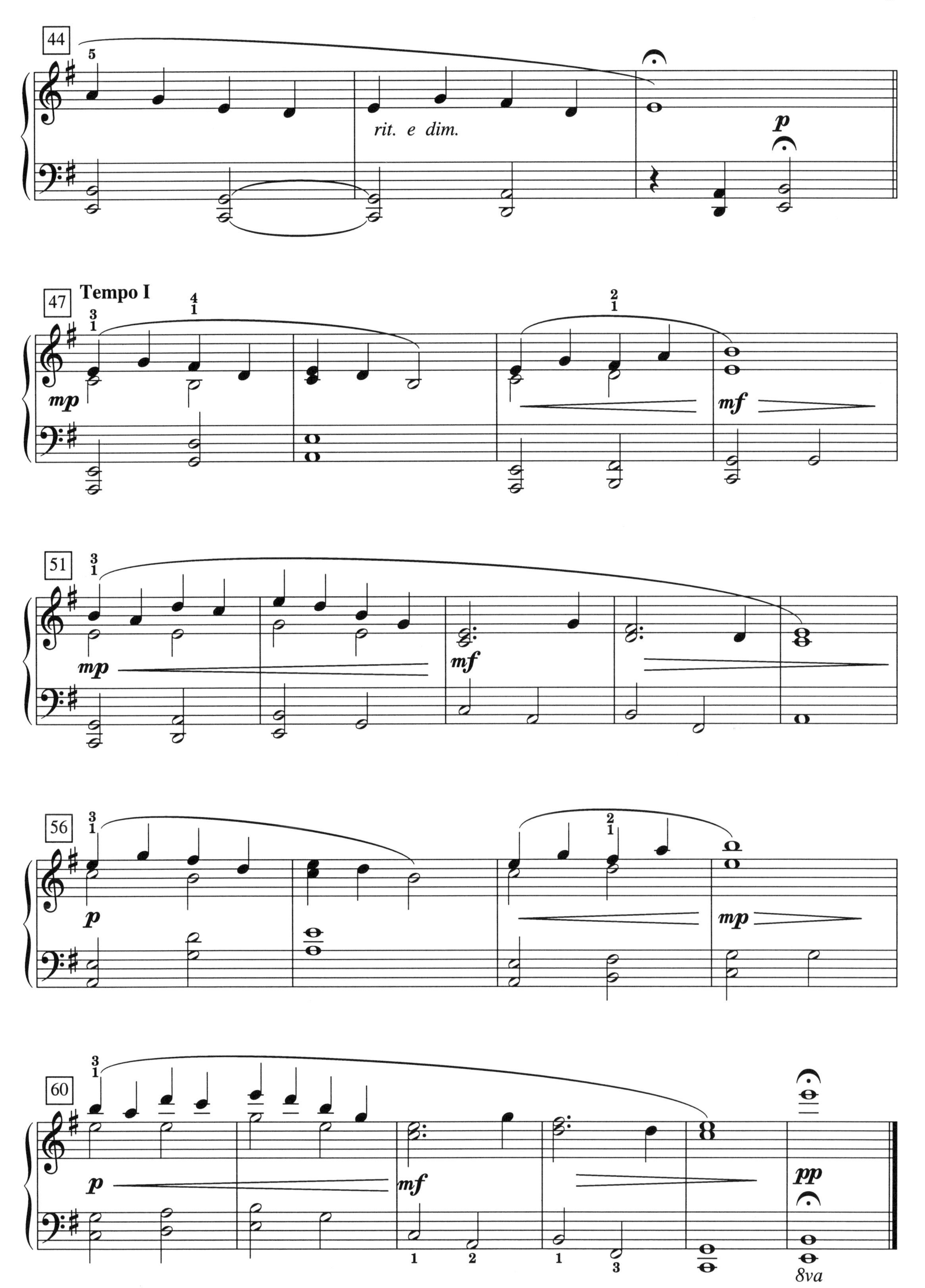
44
rit. e dim.
p
47
Tempo I
mp
mf
51
mp
mf
56
p
mp
60
p
mf
pp
8va

WILD WINDS

Ann Buys

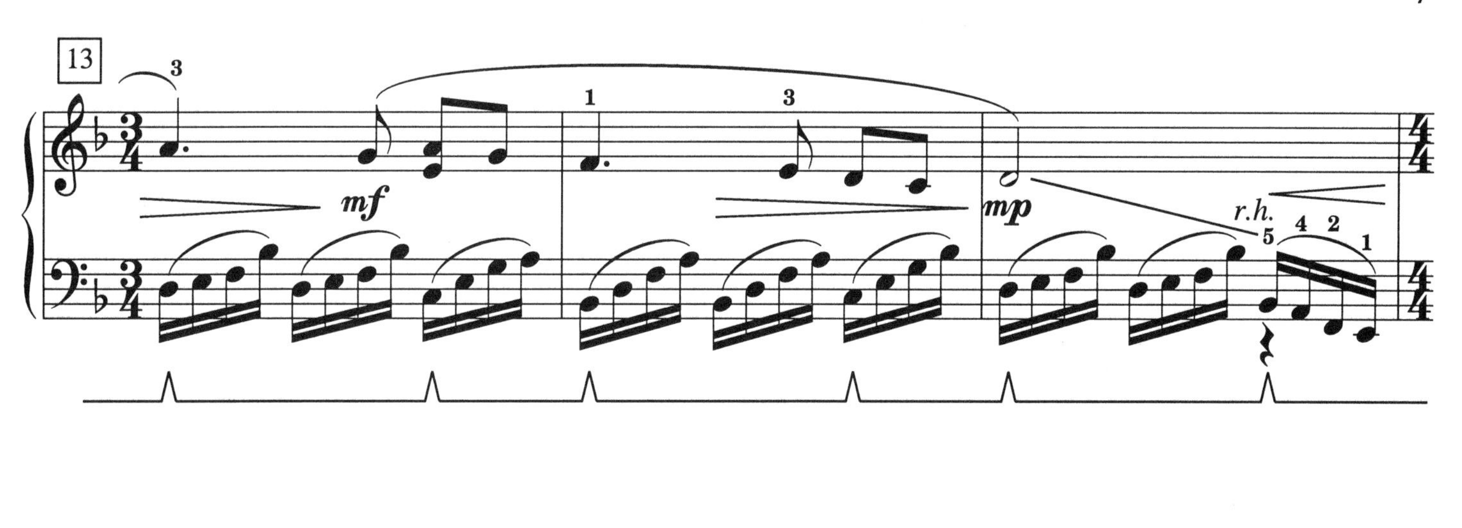
13
mf
mp
r.h.

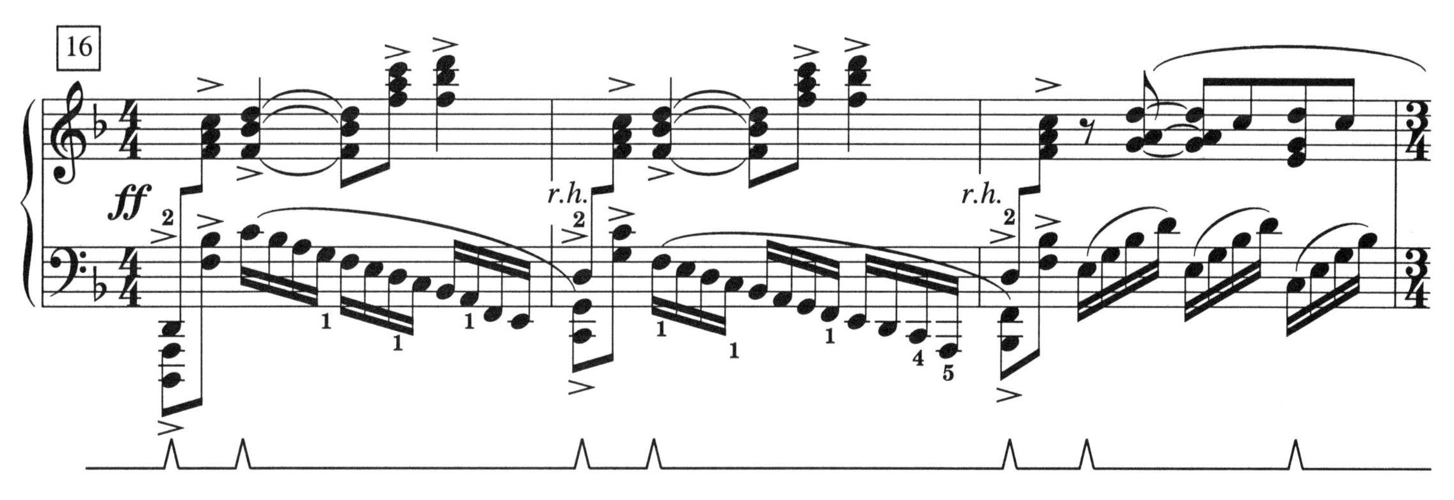
16
ff
r.h.
r.h.

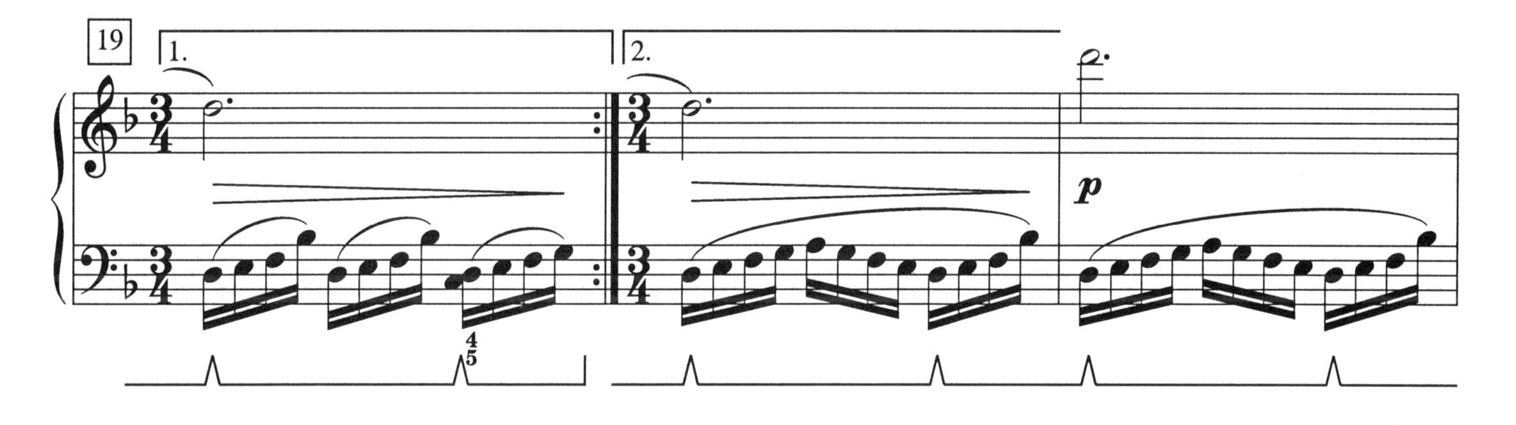
19
1.
2.
p

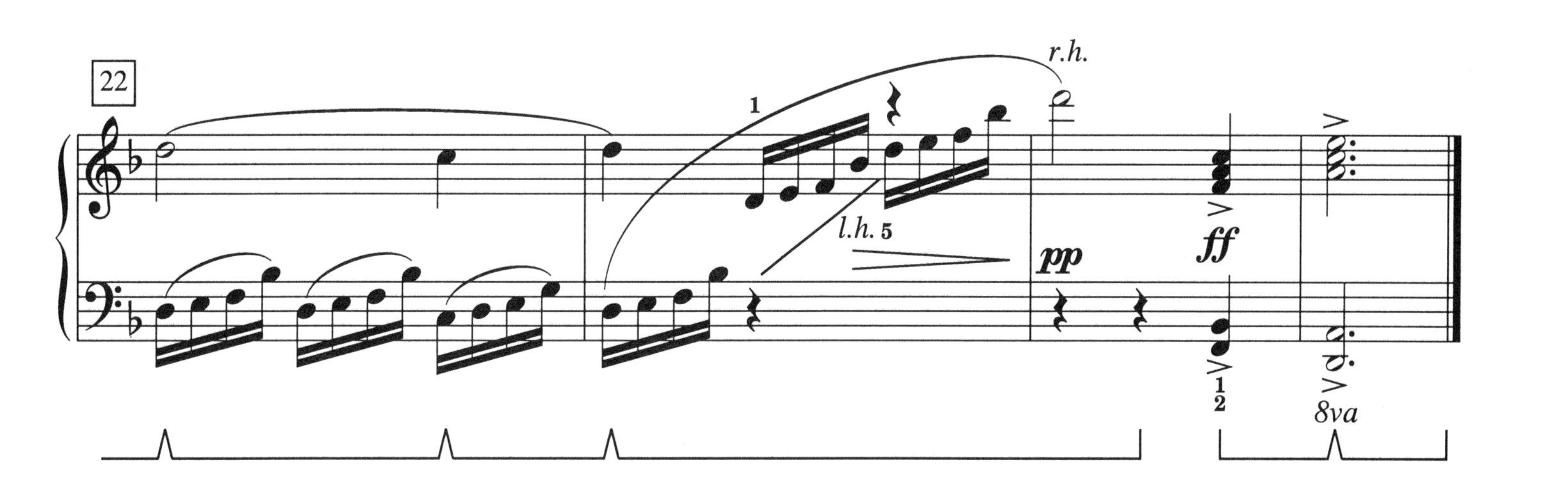
22
r.h.
l.h.
pp
ff
8va

SEGO LILY

Ann Buys

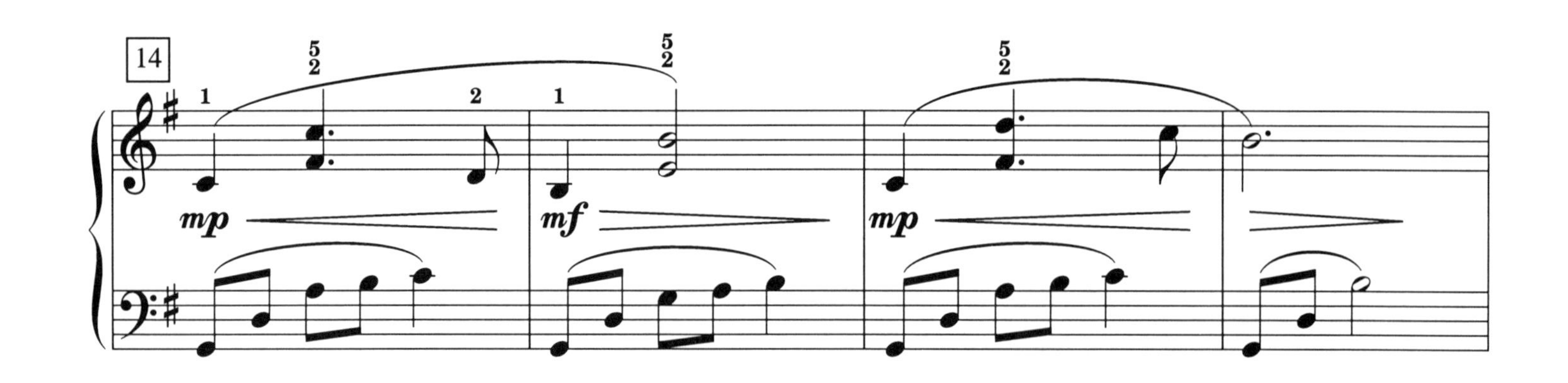

18

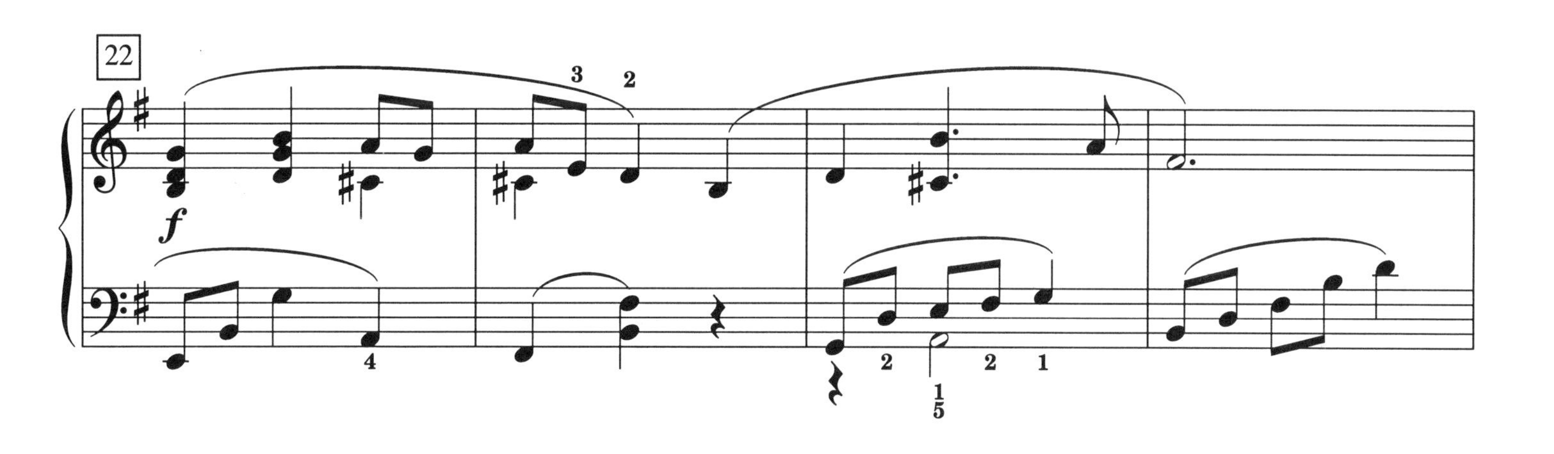
22
f

26
mf
f

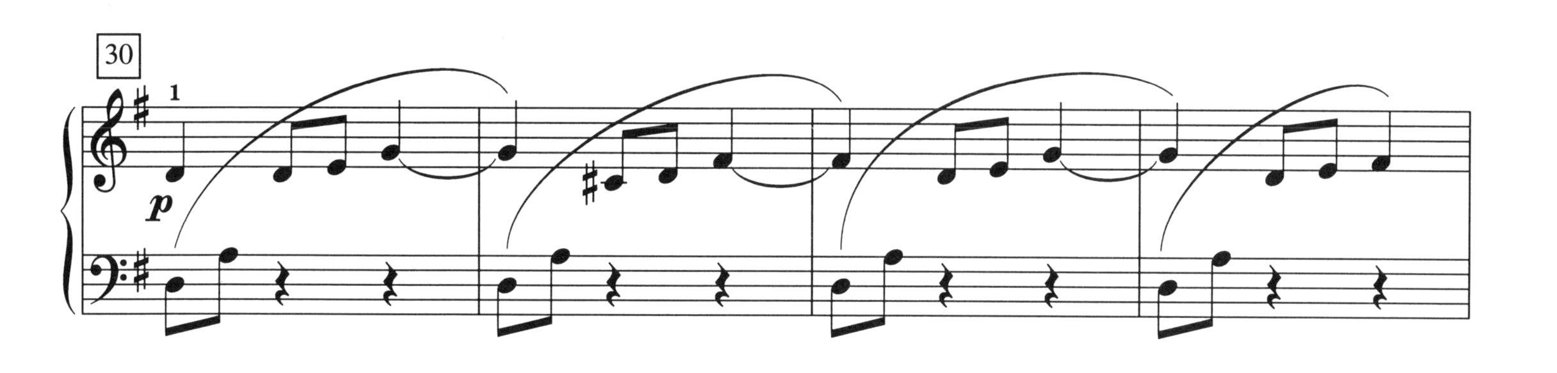
30
p

34
4
mp

38

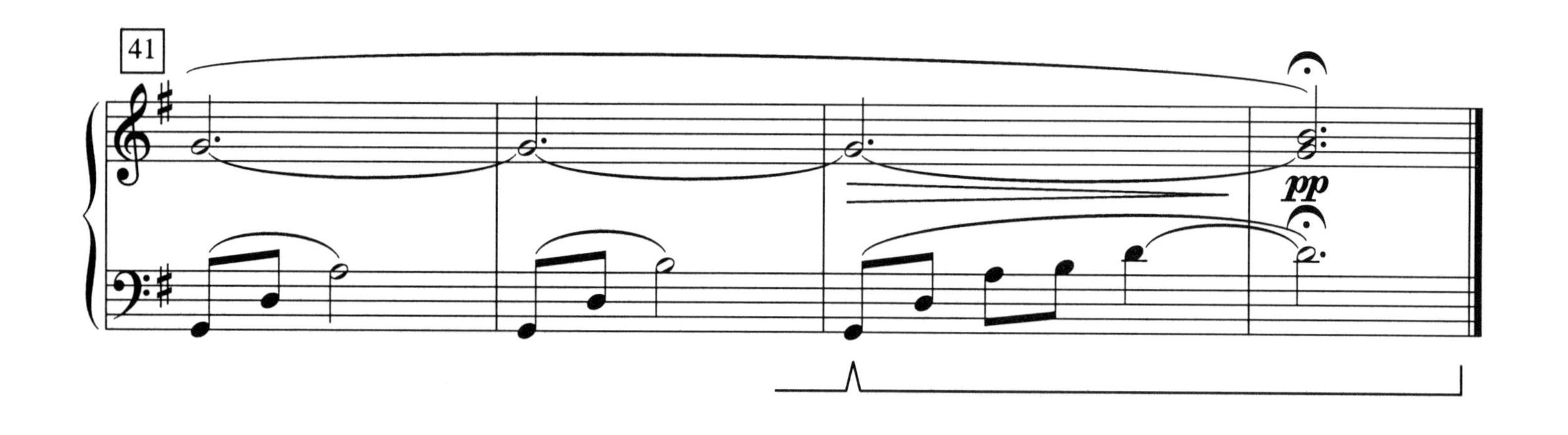
41
pp

RED ROCK BOOGIE

Ann Buys

16
mf
4
19
f
p
1
f
22
1
mf
3
1
25
2
1
4
1
f
28
mf
pedale simile

31
34
f
4
37
p
mp
40
43
mf
p
r.h.
8va

SPRING WATERFALL

Ann Buys

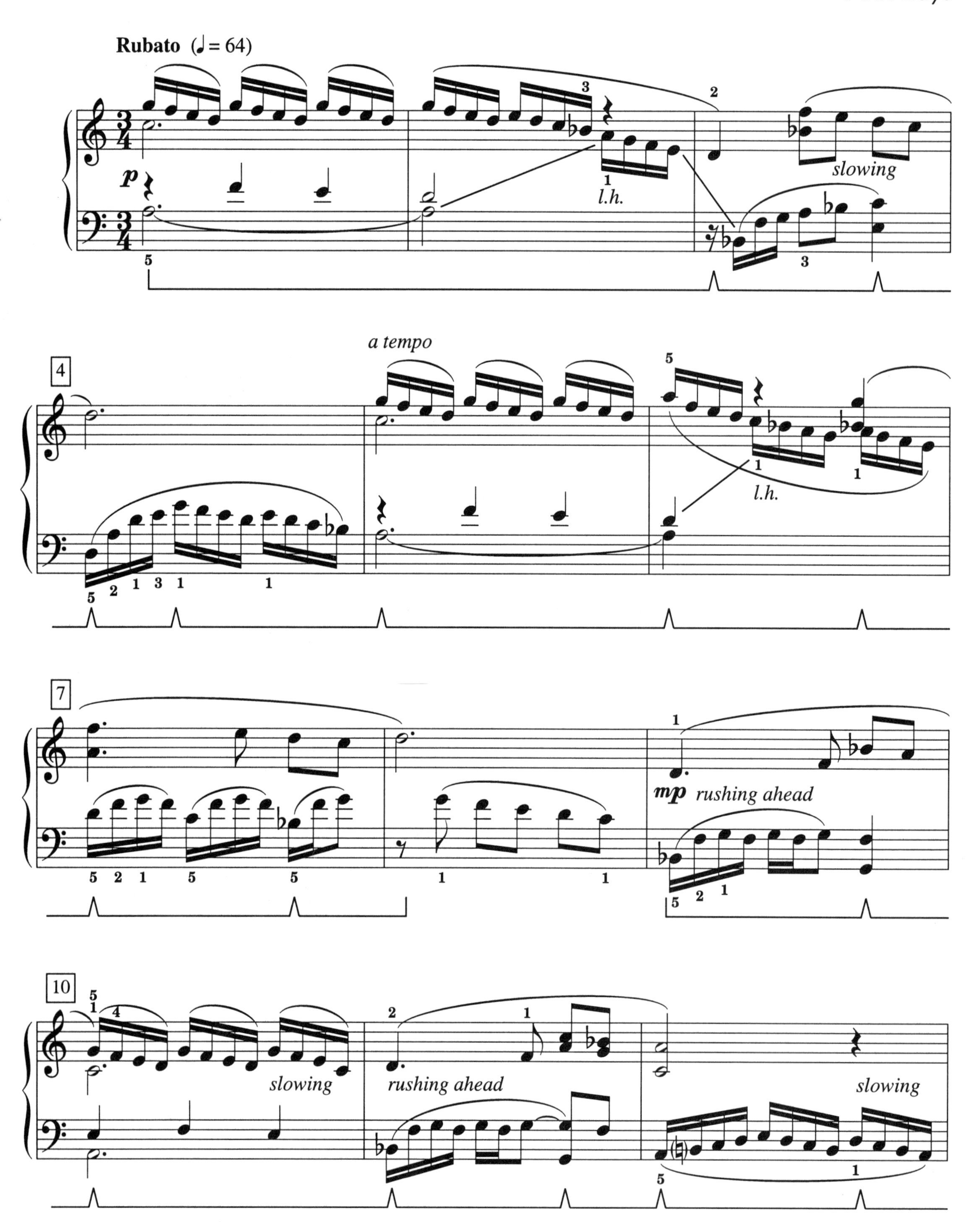

13
rushing ahead
16
Tempo I
mf rit. e dim.
19
mp
r.h.
a tempo
l.h.
slowing
22
slowing
25
a tempo
molto rit.
una corda

RIVER RAFTING

Ann Buys

16
mf
19
22
mp
p
25
mf
28

32
ff
mp
35
pedale simile
38
f
42
mf
45
mp
rit. e dim.
p
r.h.
8va

This page has been left blank in order to facilitate page turns.

AT DUSK

Ann Buys

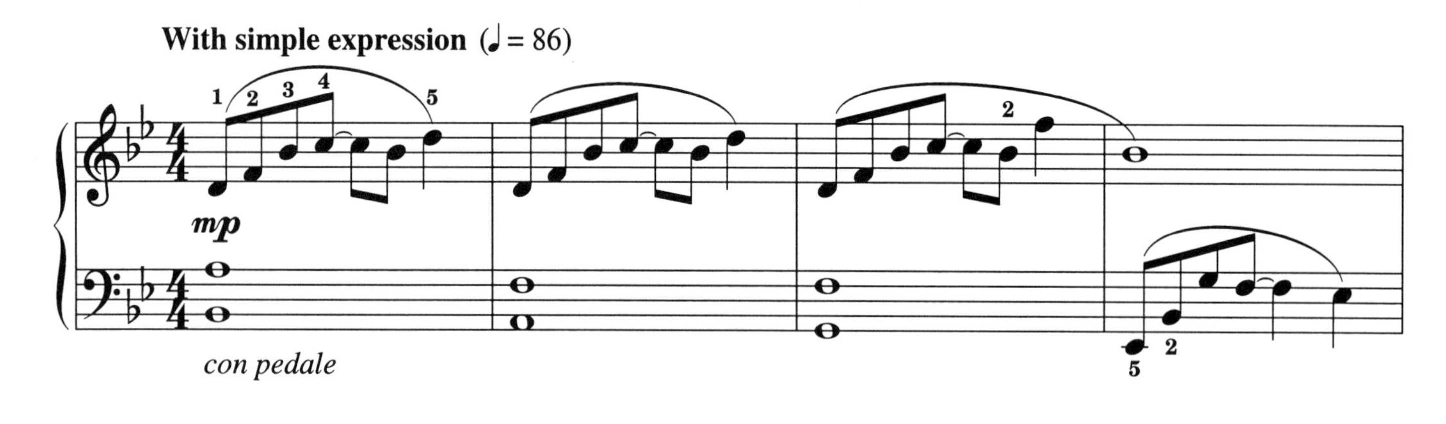

17
5-1
r.h.
p
1
2
mf
mp
5 3 1
21
r.h.
mf
25
1
3
con pedale
5 3 2 1
29
mp
32
2
5-1
r.h.
rit. e dim.
p